Summer Rain

Noel Duffy

Ward Wood Publishing
www.wardwoodpublishing.co.uk

Published by Ward Wood Publishing
6 The Drive
Golders Green
London NW11 9SR
www.wardwoodpublishing.co.uk

The right of Noel Duffy to be identified as author of this
work has been asserted by him in accordance with the
Copyright, Designs and Patent Act, 1988.
Copyright © 2016 Noel Duffy
ISBN: 978-1-908742-57-5

British Library Cataloguing in Publication Data. A CIP
record for this book can be obtained from the British Library.

Designed and typeset in Palatino Linotype by
Ward Wood Publishing.
Cover design by Ward Wood Publishing.
Artwork: Reflection of the electric light in the rain
© Nikolay Pozdeev
Supplied by agency: Dreamstime.com

Printed and bound in Great Britain by
Imprint Digital, Seychelles Farm,
Upton Pyne, Exeter, Devon EX5 5HY

For Brian Walsh and Beth Phillips
in long friendship

Contents

III. Summer Rain

Summer Rain

Telescopium

The sky had been all but named
beyond some small, studded
corners in the darkness above him.
There, at the Cape of Good Hope,
Abbé Nicolas Louis de La Caille
built his observatory after long voyage,
this the very vantage point he needed
as he set out to map the Southern Skies
into its ten thousand points of fire.
And hidden there between Corona
Australis and Sagittarius,
he thought to give this humble cluster
of stars its own name; not in honour
of some ancient god or fabled creature,
but the eye of the telescope that peers
deepest into the firmament's recesses –
this instrument so named in light,
the object of his calculating vision
and the one true God he sought
in every corner of the heavens.

I. Games of Chance & Reason

Preface

Driven in no small part by the industrial revolution, scientists in the 19th century became deeply interested in further understanding the concept of energy and how it could be harnessed to run machines, from the mass production of linen by weaving looms, to the grand promise of fast and safe travel using steam locomotives. Key to this was understanding more fully the physics of heat and how it could be exploited to do 'work'. By the 1830s Sadi Carnot and Rudolf Clausius, among others, provided the answer in their theory of classical thermodynamics. However, one thing this new theory showed was that in the act of running such machines – and, indeed, in nature itself – energy was always lost in the process of doing 'work'. Whatever you put in, you got less out. They described this (irretrievably) lost energy as entropy.

By the 1870s, the Austrian physicist Ludwig Boltzmann set out to explain all the laws of classical thermodynamics in such a way as to try to establish the *why* as well as the *how* of its operation. Using a deceptively simple starting point, he posited that atoms existed and if we measure their behaviour in vast numbers using statistical methods, all the laws of classical thermodynamics could be fully understood. His explanation also added important new detail that gave a far more nuanced basis to such a theory. In Boltzmann's refined version, the phenomenon of entropy is further crucially redefined, adding that energy always moves from an *ordered* state to a more *disordered* one as probability dictated. However, a key insight of Boltzmann's theory was that it allowed for pockets of order to exist within disorder, so long as the *overall* entropy (or disorder) of a system increased as a result. This, he believed, gave a working foundation for how the complexity of life itself (an ordered state) could arise without defying this fundamental law of entropy as he had proposed it.

The great difficulty for Boltzmann, however, was that while atoms were generally accepted as real by many chemists at this time, physics had moved as the century progressed towards a form of philosophy called positivism, which only accepted as fact statements that could be tested directly. Basing a theory, as Boltzmann had done, on something that could never be observed directly in the atom, was seen by many as breaching the very basis of good scientific practice. One of the most forceful proponents of this new positivist philosophy was Ernst Mach, a theoretical physicist and philosopher of note as we shall see. As Jacob Bronowski observed in his seminal TV series, *The Ascent of Man:* 'Who would think that only in 1900, people were battling, one might say to the death, over the issue of whether atoms are real, or not... [Science] tethered on a fine intellectual balance at that point, because had the anti-atomic doctrines won the day, our advance would certainly have been set back by decades...' As these words suggest, this issue became an increasingly central, and heatedly debated, one as the century came towards its end and the new one began.

Ludwig Boltzmann is now universally considered to have been one of the most gifted theoretical physicists of the 19th century. His theory of statistical mechanics is now taught on all university physics degree courses around the world. However, as we shall see, the path to such acceptance was far from a given in Boltzmann's lifetime and the fact that he also struggled with bipolar disorder complicated his situation considerably. It should also be noted that while Einstein's paper on Brownian Motion was published in 1905, it took several years for his work to be widely disseminated. There is no evidence (that I could find) that Boltzmann was aware of its existence in the first days of autumn, 1906.

Finally, there is a surprisingly small amount of biographical information available about Boltzmann in the English language, but I am indebted to *Great Physicists* (Oxford University Press, 2001) by William H. Cropper and, more especially, *Ludwig Boltzmann: The Man Who Trusted Atoms* (Oxford University Press, 1998) by Carlo Cercignani. Boltzmann's introductory remarks on his course on statistical mechanics are taken *verbatim* from an account by Lise Meitner, reproduced in *Lise Meitner: A Life in Physics* (University of California Press, 1997) by Ruth Lewin Sime. It should be noted that some small liberties have been taken here in the chronology of events, as well as some dramatic necessities to relay such a complex subject in a contracted form, though both are undertaken only in order to draw out the dynamic of the relationships between the characters at the heart of the story.*

---

* Clearly, in this sequence of poems, Mach is portrayed principally in terms of his fraught relationship with Boltzmann and, as such, is represented here as his adversary. He died in 1916 after a long illness. Boltzmann's student, Lise Meitner, went on to complete her doctoral studies with Franz Exner in 1905, with Boltzmann as a secondary supervisor. She was only the second woman to be allowed to undertake PhD studies in physics, aided greatly by Boltzmann's support for her. She went on to work with Otto Hahn as part of the team that discovered nuclear fission, for which Hahn won the Nobel Prize for Chemistry in 1944. She died in Cambridge in 1968, aged 89. Little is known about Henriette Boltzmann (née von Aigentler) after Boltzmann's death. She died in Vienna in 1938, aged 84.

"...a kind of memory tells us

that what we're now striving for

was once truer and nearer

and attached to us with infinite tenderness.

Here all is distance, where once it was breath."

– Rainer Maria Rilke, *Duino Elegies*

1895

Ludwig stands in the small wood-panelled
lecture room, a dozen or so students facing him
in rows. 'I ask you to place your faith in me,
for there are those who say I am a charlatan
or a fool. And some who say I am both!'
The students laugh. Ludwig smiles.
He removes his spectacles and wipes them clean,
puts them back on. 'I ask only for strict attention,
tireless strength of mind and iron discipline.
But forgive me if I ask you for something else
entirely. Your trust and even your affection.'
He looks up and holds on them. 'In turn,
I will give everything I have of myself,
my entire way of thinking and feeling.' Ludwig
spreads his hands and leans on the lectern:
'We shall begin then by making a simple
assumption and one assumption only.
That atoms exist as they most surely must
and in allowing this I will show you how
their movement and behaviour in large numbers,
when treated with statistical methods, will give us
the very foundation for all the laws of heat
and its dissipation. I call this new theory, then,
statistical mechanics.' Ludwig claps his hands
and grins. 'So, let us begin.'

*

'You see I was born on the night of the carnival
between Shrove Tuesday and Ash Wednesday.'
'And this you say gives you your moods?' 'Yes,
moods. I soar high like the eagle, then fall back down
like the chicken. My mother said it was the noise
of the revellers that disturbed my babyish dreams.'
'Too young surely to be so affected?' Mach replies,
eyeing him. 'Oh, you see I'm not sure I believe her.
I just like to tell the story by way of explanation.'
Ludwig laughs loudly and peers through his round glasses,
his eyes small and beady behind the strong lenses.
'Another drink, Ernst, or are you already sated?'
'I'm fine as I am, but go ahead as you wish.'
'With your permission then I shall have another cup.'
He turns and calls out to the passing host: 'Wilhelm,
a ruby red for me and Ernst will be having water.'
'I see you are in buoyant spirits this evening, Ludwig.'
'I am, I most certainly am. But we have cause
for celebration, do we not!' Wilhelm turns to Mach,
'I hope you will enjoy your tenure here at the Institute,
Ernst.' Mach smiles dryly, 'Oh, I already am.'
Wilhelm glances at Ludwig with a worried frown,
'A *ruby red* then for you and a water for our new colleague.'
Ludwig faces Mach again and smiles broadly.
'So what brings you here to Turkenstrasse, Ernst?
I mean, your main area of concern.' Mach sips
on his glass then puts it down. 'To prove you wrong.
So, if you'll forgive me I really must be getting along.
No need for the water then, but thank you, Boltzmann.'
Mach smiles again, turns and is gone. A woman
in an evening gown moves to Ludwig's side, his eyes
still fixed on Mach as he moves through the crowd.
'Everything well with you, Darling?' Ludwig turns,
forces a smile. 'Of course, my dear. Of course.
It'll be fine. Quite fine, I'm sure...'

1898

A young woman walks up the gravel path
of a large house carrying a box. She hesitates,
then places it on the step, goes to turn. The door
opens. A tall woman stands in the frame.
'Yes?' 'Oh, Frau Boltzmann. I am Lise...
Lise Meitner. I am a student of Professor Boltzmann.
I hadn't meant to disturb you. I'm sorry.'
'There is no need. My husband has mentioned you.
You hope to continue your studies, he tells me.'
'I am most grateful for the faith he has shown in me.'
'It is not faith he sees in you, but talent. But be careful,
for there are many who see that as a most unsatisfactory
quality in a young woman.' 'Yes, I've been told so.
And often!' Henriette laughs, eyes her a moment.
'Was there something, in particular, you needed?'
Lise remembers the box, picks it up. 'Oh... I
– the students – wanted to give the professor
this small gift. We have noticed his shoes
are a little worn.' 'Oh, I see. And these are...'
'I hope I haven't offended you.' 'Not yet.'
Henriette opens the box to reveal a new pair
of brown leather boots. She raises an eyebrow.
'He may yet accept your present, for I see
you have noticed his fondness for all things
brown.' Lise laughs out loud. Henriette smiles.
'Thank you, Lise. It is most kind of you –
and the students.' She is about to go inside
but stops: 'Though it is more usual for a wife
to try, at least, to dress her husband than his students.'
Lise flushes. 'I will make sure he tries them on.'
'Thank you, Frau Boltzmann.' Lise hesitates, then turns,
the gravel crunching beneath her feet as she gathers pace,
Henriette smiling in the porch as Lise makes her escape.

Ludwig comes into the lecture room
the small group of students huddling close,
still wearing their winter coats. 'The room
is a little cold here today, is it not?' He chuckles,
makes a show of rubbing his hands. 'It seems
because we're physicists we must therefore
be treated as prisoners of our own misfortune!'
The students laugh. 'Well then, to the physics
we shall go, in this cold, cold room'. Ludwig pulls
a deck of cards from his jacket pocket, spreads them
on the table before him. They are in perfect sequence,
suit by suit. He smiles, then gathers them up,
begins to shuffle. 'So, what is happening now?'
There is silence. 'Come, come, you must at least
try to keep up with me as we make our course.'
He keeps shuffling the deck, waits. A quiet voice
breaks the silence: 'An ordered state is becoming
a more disordered one.' It is Lise. 'Exactly, Lise.
And the more I shuffle the cards, the more disorderly
they become. Much to the relief of the card dealer
I should imagine!' The students laugh again.
'This simple trick demonstrates my concept of entropy:
how an orderly state will always return to a more
disordered one, my shuffling of the cards the action
of time on a system. It is the natural law of things.'
He smiles again. 'But surely, Professor, chance
must also allow for sequences of order to be possible
within such a disorderly condition.' It is Lise again.
'So sometimes the card player wins.' 'Ha, indeed he might!
What a clever insight. And yes, this is most correct.
This very observation shows how my theory
allows for pockets of order to exist in this
unruly universe we find ourselves to be living.
This, I believe, may also explain how life arose and,
thus, the very energetics of evolution itself.'
Ludwig throws the deck into the air, the cards

falling down like leaves to the floor all about him. 'And it is even more disorderly now, this the fate that awaits us all when the game is done.'

1900

Ludwig bumbles down the corridor, stops
and searches through his sheaf of papers.
Mach comes towards him. 'I see you are
well prepared for your lecture, as always.'
Ludwig pulls out a sheet from the mess.
'Found it... I don't refer to notes, I just like
to have them. And what is it to you, Ernst?'
'It's just a game by numbers, Boltzmann.
Nothing more. The sooner you realise that
the sooner your talent may not yet be wasted –
or you laid to ruin.' 'And what is your talent?
To knock me down?' Mach laughs.
'I'm trying to steer you straight and back
to common sense. No one has seen these atoms
and they never will. They exist only in your mind
and those of chemists. Had you not heard?'
Ludwig pulls away to the sound of Mach's laughter,
his breathing heavy as he continues down the corridor.

Ludwig sits on a park bench resting, the sunlight
dappled in the leaves and branches above him.
He watches as a group of boys gather by the water's edge,
launch their paper boats out onto the trembling surface,
each hoping their craft might catch on a steady current
as they race towards the bridge in the distance...
These, so like the paper boats he too made as a child,
each pushed out carefully from the river's edge
as he watched the fragile vessels travel downstream
and on towards the farmlands that lay beyond,
knowing as they disappeared from view
that some invisible force carried each along;
how by such small things observed, the world might
be understood, its patterns arrested in reflection
and thought, to reveal all of nature's hidden laws.
He stands up and smiles as a young boy cheers,
his boat having arrived first at the finishing mark,
then shuffles off slowly into the afternoon sunlight,
happy that boys remained the same, excited by such
simple games – how through these experiments
made, some small pleasure may still be gained.

*

'Was Darwin too not also mocked,
for his Theory of Evolution?'
Exner sits in a chair opposite Ludwig.
'Yes and he still is,' Ludwig retorts.
'By some perhaps. And we know them
to be wrong.' 'Positivism is destroying
our subject, Franz, and all of science with it.'
'I see Mach grows ever more vocal in his
criticism of you. He's a persuasive speaker.'
'I have to take him on. Make a challenge.'
'How?' Ludwig straightens in his chair.
'By beating him on his own terms.
I must bring myself to learn philosophy.'
Franz leans in close to his friend.
'Ludwig, you ask your students to trust you,
do you not, yet you do not trust yourself.'
Ludwig looks down at his hands, then up:
'Is there someone you might recommend?
Someone who might instruct me?' Franz sighs.
'There is Brentano.' 'The married priest!'
'No longer a priest, though very much still
married. He's a good man.' Franz stands,
'I shall send on his address in Florence.'
He goes to the door, then turns, 'You were right.
I mean about Lise. She has a fine mind.'
'A finer one than either of us, I'd wager.'
'I wouldn't go that far. Not yet.' He smiles.
'So will you take her on?' 'Perhaps.'
Franz goes to the door and leaves. Ludwig chuckles,
then takes a sheet of paper from a pile,
lifts it closer to his failing eyes.

1902

Ludwig sits on the bed in buoyant mood
as Henriette undoes his spotted neck-tie.
'Did you notice that Mach wasn't there?'
'Of course he wasn't, Dear. What did you expect?'
'What does it matter? I have him to the wall now.'
He reaches his hand to her blonde hair. 'And I love you
more with every day the morning sun brings.'
She touches a hand to his face. 'Dear Louis, be calm.
Try to be calm. For the carnival rages in you tonight –
and Elsa is asleep.' 'I know, I'm sorry, my sweet.'
'Mach's not going to lie down. He's not done with you yet.
You must recognise that.' 'But tonight, Henriette,
were they not sitting in the aisle as well as the seats?
And surely you heard how they clapped like thunder
when I finished my lecture. You must have,
for you were there also if I'm not mistaken.'
He pulls Henriette onto his lap and kisses her.
'I have beaten him at his very own discipline.'
'Brentano has taught you well, but you must understand
everyone likes to watch a bare knuckle dispute.
There is something too much of the circus about it.'
'But did you not hear the roar of their appreciation?'
She touches a finger to his lips. 'When he retorts, they too
will turn out in their numbers and cheer him on also.'
He looks at her with a frown. 'But tonight is mine,
is it not?' 'It is, my dear, it is. Now try to get some rest
for you will need it tomorrow.' She kisses him,
then gets up and walks to the dresser, Ludwig
still frowning on the bed behind her.

*

Ludwig stands in the department office
holding a cup of strong coffee. The others
chat in small groups as Ludwig observes.
Just as he is about to catch Franz's eye,
Mach approaches him. 'Morning, Ernst.
Here for some debate, I'm sure.' 'Me? Never.'
'Well *never* has never stopped you before.'
Mach laughs. 'You can't have it both ways,
Ludwig. You must know that.' 'You see.
What did I say? Take your aim then.'
'These atoms can't be both useful 'models'
as you call them on the one hand and yet
still real things, it seems, on the other –
which you now insist upon in your lectures.'
'I didn't realise you were there, Ernst.'
'I know you are trying to find a course between us.
I see that, but you must know that no one,
on either side, will accept such a compromise.'
'You mean, you won't.' 'No, I mean those
who support your claims and see you
as their last spokesman. You should stick
by your guns and leave philosophy well alone.'
'I expected a better battle from you.'
'They are either there or they are not.
And they're not.' Mach sips his coffee.
'Though I commend your effort to at least
try to find some common ground between us.'
'Keep your colours nailed to the mast, Ernst,
and stick by them. Civility never suited you.'
Mach seems taken aback by Ludwig's tone.
'I'm trying to say that, whatever you believe,
we are still colleagues who should behave
with some decorum toward each other.
There were remarks that you made, I've heard.
About me.' 'Have you lost your faith, Ernst,
in your calling now that I can face you finally

on your own conditions?' Franz glances anxiously
towards them, is about to approach as Mach
tenses: 'For someone who so fervently espouses
the nature of chance, you seem to think
the same rules may apply to philosophy also.
They do not.' Ludwig leans into him:
'It is not chance I speak of, but probability.
There is a world of difference and you
bloody well know it.' Ludwig now red-faced
with anger, pokes a finger at Mach's chest, 'Atoms
have existed since the beginning of time
and will still be here when you and I
have long been returned to the dust
we came from.' Franz guides Ludwig
away from a shocked Mach. 'Ludwig,
control yourself. This isn't the first time.'
'He sets out to attack me and then *I* must leave.'
Franz moves him towards the door.
'We will talk later. When you've calmed down.'
Ludwig pulls away from him roughly and goes,
the room in total silence now.

*

Ludwig sits in his study by the window,
the stack of correspondence with Brentano
lying on the desk beside him. He takes
a sheet of paper from a pile and raises
his pen. 'Dearest Franz,' he begins,
but cannot find the words to go on.
He had thought that perhaps philosophy
was his true calling, all the ideas of a life
a preparation to make an attempt on the summit.
But he is no philosopher, he knows that now.
He has been playing at a game in thinking
that this was where the true battle waited.
He can't help but notice that each week
fewer people come to his lectures, the benches
half empty, no one in the stairwell now;
no newspaper men or ovations, just politeness.
To think that once he thought himself great,
that he had earned his place at the table.
Now all seems lost; lost to him in dispute
and the over-labour of duties. He knows
this cannot go on, that he falters more
with every step he tries to take, each ending,
it seems, in failure and regret.

*

'Mach is right. I have placed myself
in a compromise by trying to please
both sides, yet neither accepts my position.'
'You were attempting to build a consensus.'
Ludwig sits opposite Franz in his study.
'I should never even have bothered. And now,
the Americans champion Mach as though
he were the very messiah of logic incarnate.'
'The tide may yet turn.' 'Yes, it has turned
and against me. Don't you think I can't see that?'
Franz can see his mood descend. He looks towards
the window and gets up, walks to where a cage lies.
'Rabbits? When did your little friends arrive?'
Ludwig looks up and glances at them.
'Elsa wanted them but Henriette wouldn't
have them in the house. I told her
I would keep them out of her domain
and in my study.' Ludwig smiles, despite himself.
'I'm sure Elsa is happy.' 'Happy, certainly.
Does she disturb me from my work? Yes,
but only five times a day.' Franz laughs,
'Not all things are so serious then, are they?'
'I wish I had the mind of a rabbit and not
my own. I might have more tranquillity
and peace of spirit.' 'Not to mention...'
'Stop, Franz. I fear you are about to
make me blush.' 'I'd never! So,
what are their names?' Ludwig grins:
'Shrove Tuesday is the white one
and Ash Wednesday, the black.' Franz laughs.
'Elsa calls them Happy and Lucky,
and I'm inclined to agree. They get fed
and their purpose alone is to amuse us all.'
'I can see how that might help everyone.
Both you and your delightful daughter.'
Franz sits back down opposite Ludwig.

31

'I'm done, Franz, I'm done for. No one
seems to take me seriously anymore.
They invite me to conferences and let me
have my word, then courteously converse
before running away. I don't know why
I even try.' 'Ludwig, you are choosing
to see only those who disagree with you.
There are many who support you also.'
'Easier to support from a safe distance than
place your head on the block. Which seems
to be my role now in this whole unholy mess.'
'Only if you wish to see yourself as such.'
Ludwig grunts, waves away Franz's comment,
'As if it were that simple. If I stop now
everything I've done will be for nothing.'
Franz shakes his head, not sure what more
can be said.

*

Lise walks the gravel path to the door
and knocks. After a moment Henriette appears.
'I'm sorry to disturb you, Frau Boltzmann.
It's just the professor missed our meeting –
this morning.' 'Poor Ludwig is not himself today.'
'I'm very sorry to hear that... I didn't mean to...
intrude.' 'Lise, you must know by now
that Ludwig's mood swings have become worse.'
'Yes... I just hope he will be well soon.'
'He works too much with his teaching
and these lecture tours he does – not to mention
his administrative duties. I've tried to get him
to slow down, but there is no point to it.
I believe him, you see, to be exhausted.
You must understand that.' 'I do, Frau Boltzmann.
I beg your forgiveness for the intrusion.'
Henriette forces a smile. Lise goes to turn, then:
'I hope the professor will soon feel himself again.'
Henriette steps from the hallway to Lise.
'Those who mock him tear out his very heart.'
She walks back a pace, then turns, 'Daily.'
Lise is taken aback by her vehemence.
Henriette seems to catch herself. 'Thank you,
Lise, for calling. I know, for you, that it is
concern that brings you to this house.
The same cannot be said of others.'
Henriette closes the door firmly behind her.
Lise remains standing in the porch,
then slowly turns away and walks.

*

Ludwig is searching his pockets as he stands
at his office door, pulls out a handkerchief
and blows his nose noisily just as Lise comes by.
'Ah, Lise. You caught me at a rather inelegant
moment.' He laughs heartily. 'Tell me now,
how are you getting along – with Exner?
Settled in, I trust.' 'Yes, very much.
I find he gives clear instruction and has placed
his trust in me as you have.' 'As he should.'
Ludwig laughs again, 'Well, good then,
I shall see you this afternoon for our own discussion.'
Ludwig is about to go in as Lise touches his arm.
He turns surprised. 'Yes, Lise?' 'Professor,
did you not hear the news about Professor Mach?'
'What of him? Is he your supervisor now also?
Nothing that man could do would surprise me any longer.'
Lise bites her lip. 'He had a stroke, Herr Professor.
Yesterday evening at his home, or so I heard.'
Ludwig stops in his track, his door half open.
'A stroke?' 'Yes. He is said to be gravely ill.'
Ludwig stays frozen for a long moment, then:
'I'm very saddened to hear it. Poor Mach.'
Lise hesitates, not sure what she should say.
'Shall I still see you this afternoon or... perhaps...'
Ludwig seems utterly thrown, tries to gather himself.
'Yes... Yes... this afternoon. Thank you, Lise.'
He goes inside and closes the door behind him,
stands staring at the rain streaking the windowpane,
then steadies himself against the frame of his chair,
pulls loose his necktie and gasps for air.

1903

Ludwig strides through the park,
his heavy bulk framed in autumn sunlight,
these trees and lakes and paths
that once gave such delight to him
seem now only to add to his anguish
as they drop their litter of foliage
on the paving all about him. He shuffles
his way along, thinking only of Mach
and how the world had turned on him,
it seemed, in the chime of a clock.
And was it not he, Ludwig himself,
who first claimed that all ordered states
must dissolve in time into a more
disordered one – his own mind
now seeming to follow this course
as all natural things eventually must.

1905

Ludwig stands in the small wood-panelled lecture theatre
as before, the students facing him in rows. 'I ask you
to place your faith in me, for there are those who say
I'm a charlatan or a fool. Or some who say I am both!'
The students laugh. Ludwig smiles. 'I ask then only
for your strict attention, tireless strength of mind
and iron discipline. In turn, I will give everything I have
of myself, my entire way of thinking and feeling.'
He pauses for a long moment, seems to hesitate.
'We shall begin then by making a simple assumption
and one assumption alone. That atoms exist and in
allowing this I will show you how their movement
in large numbers, when treated with statistical methods,
will give us the very foundation for all the laws of heat
and its dissipation.' A student interrupts, 'But Professor,
a theory rests on its assumptions or so we have been
instructed.' Ludwig seems caught. 'It does, indeed.
What a good education we have given you.' 'But
the existence of atoms is yet unproven and most surely
never will be.' 'I am using a deductive argument,'
Ludwig replies wearily. 'But we already have a theory
that serves all necessities in classical thermodynamics.'
'There are differences...' There is a long awkward silence.
Ludwig takes off his glasses and cleans them, puts them
back on. 'For those who prefer the positivist position,
as you clearly do, we may also proceed if we think of atoms
simply as useful models.' Ludwig tries to force a smile:
'I call this new theory then, statistical mechanics.'
He pauses for a long moment, then: 'So let us begin.'

1906

'Louis, will you not get your suit cleaned?'
'I don't have time. It will delay our return.'
'Come for a swim with Elsa and I, will you?
It will relax you and you enjoy the water.'
'You go, I have lectures to prepare.
My course on philosophy begins tomorrow
at first light.' Henriette lifts the suit from the bed.
'Then I shall have it cleaned for you.
You must look your best for your students,
must you not?' She moves close and kisses him.
'Are you sure you won't come, Dear? The doctor
said you should try to get some rest.' 'I'm fine.
You and Elsa will enjoy your time together.'
Henriette smiles weakly in return, pulls away.
'It would be more fun if you were there with us.
You know how I have always wanted to visit Duino
and swim in the clean, sea air.' 'I know, my dear,
but I will be here when you return.'
Henriette takes the suit, walks to the door.
'We will be back before too long.' 'Do you...
love me still, Henriette? I mean, despite everything?'
Henriette comes back, touches a hand to Ludwig's face.
'Why do you ask such a question? Of course I do.
I always have.' She studies him a moment, then
pulls away from him and moves to the door, turns:
'And I always will.' She smiles quizzically, then leaves,
Ludwig's gaze following her as she disappears.

*

Henriette and Elsa walk back towards the hotel
through the gardens, a light rain now falling
around them. Henriette leans down close to
the heavy blossoms, breathes in deeply.
'How I love the musk of roses rising up
after summer rain. Don't you, Elsa?'
'Yes, Mama. It is nature's own perfume.'
'It is.' Henriette straightens again. 'We'd better
go back. Your father is expecting us.'
They walk to the entrance and past the reception,
continue down the corridor towards their room.
Henriette approaches the door, opens it,
'Well, your suit is ready for tomorrow, Louis.'
She enters, cries out at the sight of his feet
dangling inches above the wooden floor,
his brown shoes untied and placed below.
She turns and pushes Elsa back through the door,
lets loose a howl as she presses her to the wall,
'Ludwig, dear love, what have you done?
What have you done...' Elsa pulls away, breaks free
from her mother, rushes down the corridor screaming.
Henriette slides down along the wall, sinks
to the floor, 'Oh, what have you done to us all,
my dear love... what have you done?'

1907

Henriette sits in the parlour, the clock
ticking against the bare walls and floor.
She just stares ahead until a knock is heard.
It is Franz. 'Hello, Franz'. Henriette
doesn't look at him. He sits down opposite her.
'There is something I need to show you.'
She turns towards him finally, smiles
weakly. 'There is this young scientist by the name
Einstein.' 'I've never heard of him.
Where does he teach?' Franz coughs.
'Well, he works in the patent office in Berne,
though not for much longer, I should imagine.'
'What is it to me?' Franz opens his leather case,
takes out several sheets. 'This is his paper.
On Brownian Motion.' 'The erratic
movement of pollen in a suspended fluid.
I studied physics once myself. You do
remember that, don't you, Franz.' 'Of course.
Which is why I know you'll understand
its significance.' 'What has he to say then,
this Einstein?' Franz leans in closer,
lowers his voice. 'He has demonstrated,
using probabilistic methods, that pollen's
peripatetic pathway in a fluid occurs
precisely because its natural course is deflected
by molecule-sized objects – rather like a pin ball
bouncing from one direct impact to another!'
Henriette grabs the paper from him,
glances at it, scanning urgently. 'It's
as strong a proof you as you could hope to find
to confirm the very existence of atoms. I shall
leave you to read it'. Franz straightens, goes to leave.
'Has Mach accepted the argument?' Franz hesitates.
'No, not Mach. But everyone else who matters.'
Henriette stands up also, pulls him close to her,

'Thank you, Franz. Perhaps we may all now rest. Now we may finally rest.' They hold each other in the late morning sunlight, rock together slowly in time-punctured silence.

II. Into the Recesses

"A lake carries you into recesses of feeling otherwise impenetrable."

– William Wordsworth

Shapes That Fit Together

The two elements exist
as though predestined
to make a perfect fit,
like a see-saw pivot the molecule
bent into a fixed contour –
one oxygen with its
partially empty shell, coupling
with two hydrogen atoms
each angling from the side –
this their own unique
and necessary marriage
at the scale of the tiny,
the weak charge each carries
enough to draw these molecules
together, grouping them
into a liquid cluster
giving us water, the cloud
that hangs in the sky above,
the rain that falls around us all;
a substance so pure it carries
no taste or smell, it the base
receptacle for the elements
that hide in its embrace,
supporting all the living things
in a given place.

That Which Lives Within

Simple yet extraordinary:
their tiny, snaking flagellum
propelling them forward
into the recesses of the invisible
world in which they move,
the faint odour of ammonia
surrounding them as they couple,
reproduce and divide again,
creating something infinitesimally
different than that which went before
deep in the dark waters
of the lake, unseen by the light
of the human gaze in this underworld
of minute size.

Molecules in Motion

The molecules move, slide and cajole,
so many of them the mind couldn't count
or comprehend it. They acquire
a new character as they move in numbers,
the fluid mechanics of slipping water
played out in complex differentials
hidden beneath the languorous surface,
the river wrestling to reach its own order
buried deep in eddies and currents
reaching for an elegant union, the waters
flowing downriver towards the lake
and the human scale of the waiting landscape.

Surface Tension

Water too has a skin,
that membrane that separates
its world from our own, the meniscus
that trembles in the light
late evening breeze, not breaking it
but forming small rivulets
upon its surface, a flickering
of light playing on the eye
separating our world from theirs:
the kingdom of water,
the kingdom of air.

The Leap

In the late months of every year they must face
the perennial ordeal: to make the long journey back
from the wide ocean's deep to the freshwater lakes
in which they were spawned and will, in turn, spawn.
Between them and their passage upriver
the salmon leap, that terrifying obstacle
that must be confronted, each attempt against it
a life-sapping assault of current and granite.
So they burrow deep then soar from their element
before crashing back down into the churning water,
the scars along their flexing bodies a previous course
tested, tried and conquered. But when they fail
they drift awhile and languish in the shallows, regaining
their strength before facing again what has to be faced,
more wily this time of the path that might be taken
to overcome the barrier that blocks their course
to the still-water reed-pools of their birth.

That Which Lives Beside

The wolf prowls in dense undergrowth,
sinews and muscles tensing,
its green eyes fixed intently forward
as it watches the fox's every movement,
stalking ever closer to the river's edge
and its victim, a slow-stepping navigation
through the thicket in near silence
as it moves in the twilit shadows. The young fox
sniffs and forages oblivious, the wolf creeping
closer still and setting herself for the kill,
pouncing suddenly and fiercely upon him,
his neck whiplashed as he is pinned down
by brutal force, the burnt-orange of his fur
bloodied at the throat as the wolf's jaw snaps,
takes hold. The vixen appears from nowhere,
snarling and hissing and biting by instinct,
but has no way to overpower the creature
or push her back into the dark forest she came from.
She backs off finally, the damage
already done, her cub lifeless on the river's edge
as she retreats warily towards the safety of the woods,
the wolf already ripping and pulling at the carcass
dripping its blood onto the muddy gravel.

Triple Point

The three boundary lines
converge on the phase diagram
to an exact point, describing water
in its three states, this meeting place
a precise measure of temperature
and pressure, hovering just above zero –
the mist that rises up above the lake's surface,
a lingering vapour; the crystalline flower of ice
that glistens; the soft, cold touch of liquid –
all co-existing by some natural magic
in the near-freeze of the autumnal evening,
the water shape-shifting from one form
to another in a delicate balance, it being
all things at once as sometimes
the laws of nature will permit.

Snow Over Grasmere

The snow falls down in cascading pleats
catching in dried leaves and branches
as it slowly drifts onto the forest canopy,
floating downward from the darkening sky
in eddies and currents, and descending into
our element. It softens the landscape
to a cushioned layer, soon turning all
to white by the river's edge. A solitary falcon
swoops down from the flurry, sweeps across
the whitened world below, scrutinises
the frozen scene, then takes to wing and disappears,
the snowflakes continuing to land in turn,
dissolving in clusters on the water's brim,
returning to their element in a different form,
the singular structure of each untangling
into the molecules of their making, melting to
a common unity before forever fading within it.

A Penny for a Pelt

The stark treeline makes
a charcoal boundary
between two fields,
the landscape stripped
of all embellishment
in the low spring sunlight.
A crow shifts in the branches
then takes to flight marking
its inky trajectory against
the weak daylight.
A solitary boy stands alone
in the ice-shook scene,
oils his gun-barrel then lifts
his eye to the sight, ready
to take aim at a rabbit
or fox, one clean shot
all that it takes to strip
their carcass for a pelt.

Rain Over Beacon Tarn

The cycle continues as it has always done,
the moisture carried up invisibly from the sea
gathering in a darkening cumulus
then drifting southward over the Eastern Fells.
And when a certain density of saturation
has been reached the cloud lets loose
its cargo of rain, starting lightly
in a gentle drizzle, then building suddenly
to a deluge. The heavy raindrops fall
across the landscape, over the pine trees
and cedar groves, the valleys and fells; and down
over the waters of Beacon Tarn, drop-dropping
on the surface in an increasing pulse, its staccato
marking small explosions on the exterior face
as it rejoins the mass of water in a cycle
that repeats as it will always do, supporting life
and nature by these circulations, like blood
passing through the heart's chambers.

Otter at Rydal

She moves quickly from the holt towards the river,
the snow plotting her footsteps over frozen ground
and foliage. She slinks into the water, mammal
but river-tied, sliding outward into the tensing current
and drawn slowly downstream by the river's muscle.
She ducks beneath the water before surfacing again,
inspects the bank with a fleeting glance, her fur
greased to a skullcap as she looks about a moment
then goes under again, her two dark eyes now
two dark windows onto the watery gloom below
as she smoothly descends into her second world.

Storm Over Skiddaw

The clouds gather darkly
above the fells and lakes,
brought in from the coast
and over Derwent. The sheep
huddle together in small clusters,
the wind blustering and chilled
as diagonal rain falls down
heavily about them. The lambs
nestle in close to their mothers
on the bare-laid hillside, baying
and seeking out their heat
against the cold wind and sleet
that drives and drives – only some
strong enough to survive.

Tynewere Waterfall

The water moves downriver
in a slow drift before gathering strength
as it approaches the waterfall's cliff,
pressed over the precipice by the weight
of water gathering behind it, reaching
the tipping point to a rushing descent,
falling in a cascade of quicksilver
force, churning up a white froth as it
impacts the granite basin below before
finally escaping the waterfall's grip,
moving downstream towards the valleys
and lakes – and the villages beyond,
of Haltwhistle and Haydon Bridge,
as it slows again to a cantering measure.

That Which Lies Beneath

The night-fisherman casts his line out into the twilit
darkness and into the tranquil waters of the shallows,
the touch of its hook upon the surface disturbing
the boundary and stirring the creatures beneath,
his fly bait luring the old trout that lurks down
in the gloaming, twitching and tensing at the smell,
and sliding slowly upwards towards the waiting snare,
caught and hooked as he makes his lunge,
his jaw impaled and torn on the sharp metal edges
as he is pulled upward fiercely by a tightening line.
He fights with every sinew in his body, tears
and flexes and tears again against his own entrapment,
the scars along the length of his mouth mementoes
of previous battles fought and won against the upper
kingdom, searing pain now his only chance of escape
from the clasp that holds him in a grip, a final ordeal
for the old soldier of the deep, the agony and instinct
that still rages against the wounding intrusion of the hook
sinking deeper into flesh with every tugging jolt he makes,
drawing him in and upward from his watery element
into the alien light of the moon rising over Windermere.

Cloud Reflected on Water

The bowl of the sky
is cupped in the lake's basin,
the upper world projected
down into the recesses,
a unity forged between sky
and deep water, coupled
in reflection and a cast of light,
the strata-cumulus hanging overhead
rippling on the water's surface,
two realms conjoined and balanced
in a single image: the world above us;
the world below.

III. Summer Rain

Muriel

Jesus who no longer lives with us
pray for us...

I was so near to true happiness
once, that bright morning
I chose Christ's love, my
wedding dress a habit not a veil
when I kneeled with the other sisters
at the altar rail, made
our solemn promise in prayer,
I felt I was so near

Jesus who no longer lives with us
pray for us...

I was so near to true happiness
once, until a door closed in my heart,
the hesitation that rises up unknown
from some dark well, hidden low,
my sister married in white brocade,
a decent man by her side,
I envying them their everyday vows
and the comfort each in the other found –
the children they brought
into their home

Jesus who no longer lives with us
pray for us...

I was so near to true happiness
once, until I grew ever lonelier
in my work, the tasks assigned to me
too great to be a blessing,
the girls in purple pinafores
sat straight in their chairs,
tense to be home while reciting prayers,
thinking of boys.
They showed no love for me.
I was hard in my ways

Jesus who no longer lives with us
pray for us...

I was so near to true happiness
once. So close I could reach out
and touch His wounds. I look up
to the stained glass windows' arch
and the fractured vision
of His suffering on the Cross,
that seems to threaten now to shatter
with my disbelieving gaze upon it.
Did He suffer for nothing,
on Calvary's Mount?
Is this my pride made doubt?

Jesus who no longer lives with us
pray for us...

I was so near to true happiness,
once. I stand now and genuflect
and bless, then shuffle past two women
mumbling rosaries, grey and old.
Are we all forgotten in the end,

when we are returned to dust,
all this love gained or lost
exhaled in one final breath,
released through the mercy of death?

Jesus who no longer lives with us
pray for us...

I draw over my gabardine,
and pull tight the belt, the rain
drum-tapping upon the steps
as I make my way back onto the street.
I ask that it may wash away my Sin,
that I may believe in Him again

Jesus who no longer lives with me
pray for me...

Sophie

I feel like I'm held together
by tape and string waiting here
in the rain for the bus to come.
I thought this tree would give
more shelter, but the water's dripping
down through it, my hair all soggy
and matted now. Stupid thing.
Should've brought an umbrella,
been prepared for all eventualities,
as Charlotte told me. Wanted
to look my most deluxe tonight,
put the glad rags on, hoping again
for that glancing look, down,
then back up, to hold me in a stare.
She is tall and self-composed
and quiet, her dark eyes seeming
to know what lies within me.
I speak too much but she doesn't seem
to mind; I've seen her look at me
a certain way, then smile.
How I've longed to reach my hand up
to her face, to lie down by her side.
If I wish it, it might happen tonight.
The restaurant is booked for eight,
my heart thump-thumping, tape
and string. It may fall apart
if this bus doesn't come – and soon.
Might grab a taxi instead, take the hit,
get running. She promised she was paying,
though it was me who made the proposition.
Will people stare if I reach for her hand?
Will she pull it back or let mine
rest on hers? My heart held together
by tape and string, as a bus rounds
the corner finally and comes into view –
ready to take me to her.

John

A memory of rain,
of our taxi travelling through
deserted streets at dawn,
the headlights searching out
the road ahead of us
as we made our way home.
Life seemed long.
That was how it felt to be young.

Time passed. We moved in
together, shared four walls,
watched as some friends grew tired,
the daily rituals of marriage
too much to carry. We said
it would never be us,
that we would brace ourselves
against such heavy weather.
That we were in this together.

But things changed. We moved
apart, found different rhythms
to our lives, conspired to keep
some corner of ourselves hidden,
each cut from a common source,
the curse of weariness
falling down between us.

The season's turned to rain.
The boats huddle in the harbour,
hull by hull, the staccato
of their rigging in the wind
a keening in the evening air.
I pull tight my coat and walk
the pier, try to hold back my fear,
you somewhere else without me.

We made promises to each other
that we could not keep, denied it
too long for the children's sake.

Christine

I place a drop upon the slide
then spread the blood along its length,
the bead smeared to a pinkish layer.
Not every day is bad, most bloods
are as they should be, the white
and red cells as portioned and populous
as the next, made luminous
and still by my microscope light.
I study what I see with an expert eye,
count the cells in the feathered edge
and confirm the worst – the progress
of it there in the lens, spreading
inexorably from one cell to the next.
This woman I've never known
beyond her altered chromosome.
Soon she will be laid to waste
by what I spy in this Cyclops eye,
she not knowing yet her fate
as she sits in a cafe somewhere perhaps,
the rain drumming against the window glass
a dulling, restless metronome,
she smiling as she picks up her cup,
telling her friend it will most probably
be fine. I have tried to be
as dispassionate as the lens' stare,
this blood work I do too far
from the living world to feel real,
protecting me from my own fear –
that if I look too closely there,
I might see my own daughter's hair,
my mother's smile, my husband's
glare, the blue eyes of the one I love.
Today I try but cannot escape
the mortal flaw that I reveal. I turn off
the machine to a humming click,

the backlight lingering a moment
then sinking to black – like the sky
my small office window frames
and the weight of news I must give
tomorrow.

Frank

He was a good footballer, played with the local team.
I was working then and had a car, would pack the kids in
whenever I could, take them to away games on Saturday
afternoons. He was spotted one day by an English scout.
I'd missed the match as I was on a late. I remember him
coming home that day, so worked up he could hardly
        breathe
as he hugged me in the hallway, then pulled back mortified.
We took the ferry to Liverpool for his trial with Everton,
        father
and son on a big adventure together, me as excited as him
as we talked about life in the big time if he kept his head.
He played well, but they turned him down. I should
        have tried
to keep his feet on the ground. He hardly spoke for a month
when we got home. I told him he could still make it in
        the game,
that other chances would come along – at worst he
        could play
in the Irish league for Bohs or Shels. But he'd lived for it
for so long and when it was taken away he was lost,
stopped playing, started hanging around with the
        wrong sort.
The young are so easily hurt. That was when the drugs
took hold. I told him to stay away from them, that
they would drag him down into the sewer with them.
But he wouldn't listen, the closeness we shared on that ferry
forgotten. It didn't take much time for him to get pulled in.
Fifteen years ago now, though the pain doesn't lessen.
I loved him even when he had come to hate me. Sometimes
there is nothing you can do. It rained the day we buried
        him too.
Doreen never recovered from shock of it, took to the drink,
the bottle as bad as the needle if you ask me. I told her
we had two children and not just one, Danielle a good girl

and doing well in school; but she couldn't come round,
fell deeper into her grief, never came out of it no matter
how we tried... Danielle is calling over soon with the boys.
She's a radiologist at a hospital now, calls over Fridays
after work. I'll put the kettle on then do the dishes,
have a sneaky cigarette before they get here. She doesn't
     like me
to smoke, says she's lost too many people in her life
to have another taken from her before their time. I'll just
have the one, then hide the pack away before they come.

Stephen

For four weeks I have sat in this room
in silence, studying the deep burgundy
of the walls, the blank grey screen of the television.
I noticed there was a spider in the bathroom,
perfectly still in the web of his own making.
With each visit I checked to see if he had moved.
He hadn't. I assumed he was dead.
I returned to my chair and looked at nothing.
In this way we passed our days together,
neither of us stirring from our vigil.
In July, the spider was gone.
From him I learnt the nature of patience.
I get up finally and go outside into the garden,
stand by the cherry blossom and inhale its musk,
the rain falling about us both.

Ailish

I felt the pebble of what once was
pass between us, beady and hard
and durable, as we always knew it
to be but had forgotten –
until we pulled close and kissed
and wrapped our limbs about each other,
found comfort in touch upon our bodies.
He sleeps now beside me like before,
the patter of rain on the sill making me
drowsy with its rhythm. I will sleep awhile
and rest and when we wake we will smile
across the distance that recently seemed
so great between us, remembering
what has happened today and the words
we said – that all things may be forgiven
as we kiss and pull each other closer still,
husband and wife, and lovers again.

Gerard

I live in darkness as some people say,
though sometimes it seems that flashes
of light appear on my retina, blues and greens
and reds. My doctor tells me it's my memory
of colour or perhaps some residual cone activity.
I wasn't always this way. Better to have seen
the world once, though it makes it harder
at the beginning. I was only eleven when
the darkness fell. I was playing rugby and took
a heavy blow to the head when the scrummage
collapsed down on top of me. I woke in the hospital
and thought it must be night. And it was in a way.
I wept when I heard my mother's voice
and she told me that my life would be different now.
At least it's not hereditary. I ask my children
to describe things for me. Jack is seven. He's
an imaginative guide and likes to add his own details,
like the monsters he sees in the park behind the trees
or a giraffe walking on Grafton Street. I play along,
ask him to tell me more about them: exactly how tall
the giraffe is and what he's eating. He says its
twenty feet high and chomps on the flowers
in the hanging baskets outside Brown Thomas.
It makes me smile. He'll grow up to be a storyteller.

I touch my hand to the page, need to brush up
on *Clair de Lune* for later. Haven't played it
in a while. It's peculiar the things that war gives us
like these strange cyphers on the page before me.
Night Writing they called it then, so Napoleon's
soldiers could communicate in the dark in silence.
They told me this to make it seem exciting.
And it was, in a way, though it took time to learn,
but it gave me eyes again, at least in my mind.
The first book I read was *Moby Dick*. I scanned

the first line slowly and nervously, 'Call me Ishmael'
it said. Such a funny name that I couldn't stop laughing,
then quickly read on, "... having little or no money
in my purse, and nothing particular to interest me
on shore, I thought I would sail about a little
and see the watery part of the world."
How my imagination lit up in joy when I heard
those words. We were going on an adventure
and I could already feel sea salt in my hair and *see*
the blue sea and white sails. I'll read it to Jack
when he's a little older. He likes whales also.

I'd best get to the restaurant, take my place behind
the piano, play light classical for the evening diners.
Music is a form of vision also, though I'm not sure
how many people know that. Some talk to me afterwards
who enjoyed my playing. It's nice to be heard
as well as seen. I go to the hallway and put on
my jacket, reach for my cane and black umbrella.
Jack says it's pink with yellow gorillas.
I hope he's making that up as well, but then
who can ever know anything for certain?

Richard

I wash down the body first. It is a difficult,
unpleasant task if I'm truthful, the body hard
and cold and often grimed with dried fluids.
There are ways of doing it more hygienically now
than when I started thirty years or more ago.

I've been at this trade as long as my father was
before he passed. I didn't make him, though
I promised him I would. It proved too painful
to prepare my own for the grave. A cousin came
and carried out the burden. This work it seems
is taken on by families. Who, after all, would choose
such a calling? But once you start and understand
its importance, there is a grace and dignity
to be found in its undertaking. A young woman
once died in France. It seemed she had drowned herself
in the Seine. The coroner ordered a death mask
to be made, the girl seemed so serene in repose,
the mask displayed in a hall and thousands came.
Not all partings are painful it seems.

We in this profession are not unlike detectives,
drawing clues from the remains on the gurney.
But no crime here except the natural order, to pass
from this state to another and not by violence.
I can tell by his hands he was a working man,
his skin a little tough and mottled; a smoker also
though not so heavy. He didn't carry bricks
or dig roads or trenches. I'd say by his long fingernails
he was a craftsman, these signs that others usually miss;
they generally don't look closely enough.

One gets used to it of course, like any other job,
and I take pride and care in my work. Most would fear it,
as they should. That first year I did this at my father's side,
I dreamt often that I lay on the table being prepared,
woke to think I must find another calling. A son's life,
after all, doesn't have to follow in his father's furrow.
There is a strange peace to be found, though, in such
delicate work. When you learn to stare the dead in the eye,
you have crossed a certain boundary that others dread.
You make your peace with it and learn to live.

The family usually pick a favourite suit and tie,
though lately some men are buried in football jerseys.
It is a practice I'm not fond of. One should face
the Maker in the correct attire. God after all
is not a football player. In any case, it's their choice
and perhaps more honest in the end. So many men
who never wore a tie are laid down forever wearing one.

I clip the nails and clean away the dirt, compose
the hands into a serene clasp. The mouth and face
are the most important though. I try to replace
the anguished look of parting with a tranquil countenance,
so that those who loved him may look down in the parlour
and see their father or brother or husband there,
instead of the death-moment etched in a grimace.
We mostly die with our mouths wide open, our last breath
expelled naturally outward, released into the wide expanse
to *something*. In this I ardently believe, my work
the last act upon a life, before the burial mass and grave...

He was old enough in any case, lived a good and
        meaningful life,
I hope, with its share of happiness and grace. Some faces
deceive of course, but this man seems gentle in his temper
and was taken without great struggle as we all plead for.
There is a tenderness, in the end, in this work I do,
though matter-of-fact in its expression it must also be.

Most are afraid of the dead, I've found. It is
to be expected. It is our purpose to live, not perish.
It grows late and the sky outside has darkened to rain.
I say a prayer for the one I've just prepared,
as is my custom, no matter what life they may have lived.
We all deserve a blessing even from a stranger, the body
now ready for my son to collect in the morning
and return this man to those who loved him.

Caroline

I love the small rituals of art,
stretching out the canvas first
to a frame, making sure
the surface is taut, then
preparing it in a primer-white
for what I might choose
to paint there. I select my tubes
of colour from the tray
and mix them onto the mottled palette.
So I start with yellow, suggesting
a field, the irises in bloom
in high summer, the hint
of wind shifting among them,
swaying in waves to the careful eye
that chooses to see it. I strike
out an outline in black
for the tree-line edged along
its boundary, add some blue for
the bowl of sky that hangs above it.
I hesitate, then make a line of red
to include a solitary figure
standing in the middle, surrounded
by a sea of summer. Yet
something's not quite right.
I can't feel the sun upon her skin,
the drowsy heat and the midday
quiet. And what is she doing there,
to begin with? Is she picking flowers
for the dinner table or lost
and alone in some personal crisis?
Or one who has found new purpose
in her mind, this landscape
her heart made visible in colour?

The light's not great, the sky
in the skylight turned to grey.
The flowers in the garden
will drink and bloom. Only then
will I return to this sun-drenched
scene, when my mind can feel
the air upon her skin, the light
crisp and the vision clear;
when I know what this woman
is feeling there. For now
I stop and listen to the rain,
the soothing rhythm drumming
on the pane. I pull open
the window to let in the air,
breathe deeply of the promise
it offers. I so love the rain
in summer, the way the smell
of earth creeps up from the garden
and catches in the nose, a dark,
rich charcoal. Perhaps this is where
she really stands, this woman
now just a line among yellow:
in a rain-lit room in an empty
cottage far from the daily struggle
she once inhabited; the demands
of work and the rituals of family
that once seemed to rule her every
waking minute. I pick another canvas
from the pile stacked along
the studio wall, blank and waiting
for a truer mood. I will paint
the smell of rain instead and start
with earthen brown and red.

*

Autumn Almanac

I.

Sycamore leaves
drift down on eddies –
sky confetti.

II.

Raindrops streaking
the dirty windowpane –
fleeting rivers.

III.

Street lamps flicker on
in November twilight –
amber nightfall.

IV.

Match flares
to light the scented candle –
odour of phosphor.

V.

Water dripping
into the empty basin –
full by morning.

Acknowledgements

These poems, or versions of them, first appeared in: *The Pickled Body (Quantum Issue), The Galway Review, The Café Review (Special Irish Issue)* and *The Irish Literary Times*. A version of the poem 'Telescopium' first appeared in the anthology *Heavenly Bodies: a constellation of poetry* (Beautiful Dragons Collaborations, 2014) edited by Rebecca Bilkau. 'Triple Point' was a finalist in The Event Horizon Science Poetry Prize and subsequently appeared in *Event Horizon Magazine*.

A very special thank you must go to Professor Emerita Marcia P. McGowan for her clear-eyed appraisal and suggestions on an early draft of this manuscript. It was hugely insightful and very much appreciated, helping to guide a course forward, especially on the 'Games of Chance & Reason' section. Special thanks must also go to Beth Phillips and Brian Walsh for reading this collection (in numerous drafts) over a long period and for their untiring advice, sympathetic engagement and understanding throughout. Very sincere gratitude to James W. Wood for his friendship, fellowship and encouragement, as well as his extremely incisive close reading of the poems included here.

A word of appreciation also for Theo Dorgan, Niall MacMonagle, Shauna Gilligan, Greg O'Brien, Jason Cochrane, Mick Cregan, Mark Carter, and Iggy McGovern for keeping me going with their interest, friendship and good company over many years. Finally, as always, a very special thank you to my publishers Adele Ward and Mike Wood for the dedication, long hours and loyalty they have shown towards me.

About the Author

Noel Duffy was born in 1971 and studied Experimental Physics at Trinity College Dublin. He co-edited (with Theo Dorgan) the anthology *Watching the River Flow: A Century in Irish Poetry* (Poetry Ireland/ Éigse Éireann, 1999) and went on to win the START Chapbook Prize for his collection *The Silence After* in 2003. His debut collection *In the Library of Lost Objects* was published by Ward Wood Publishing in 2011 and was shortlisted for the Shine/Strong Award for Best First Collection by an Irish Poet. A second collection, *On Light & Carbon,* followed in 2013, again with Ward Wood. He remains in Dublin.

For more information about Noel and his work visit: noelduffy.net